A Walk Down Phonics Lane

A Walk in the Phonics Zoo

Malia,

I hope you enjoy reading A Walk in the Phonics Zoo! Don't forget to learn wherever you go!

[illegible]

Written By: Cherie Feemster
Illustrator: Jasmine T. Mills
ISBN Number: 978-0-578-89677-9

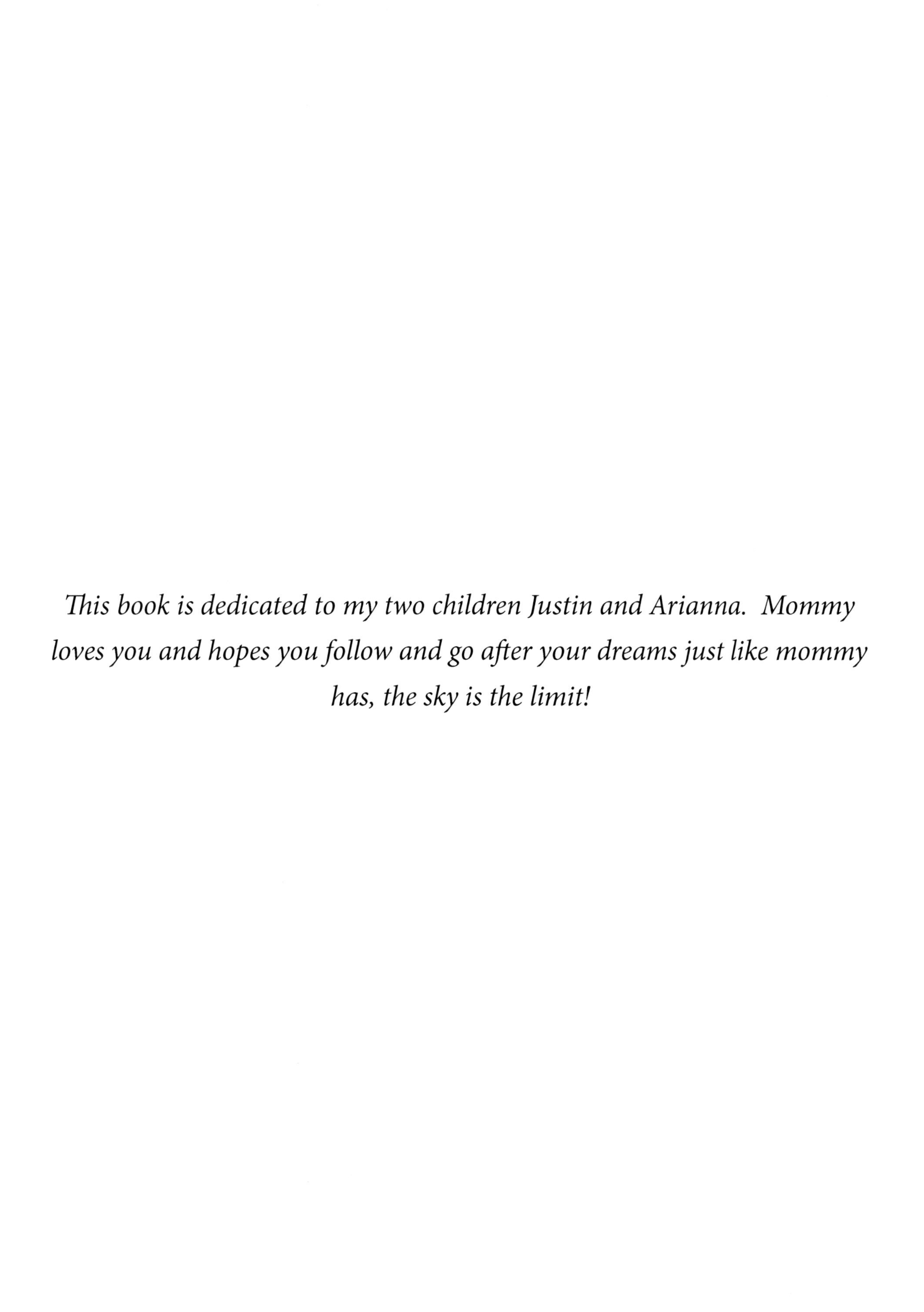

This book is dedicated to my two children Justin and Arianna. Mommy loves you and hopes you follow and go after your dreams just like mommy has, the sky is the limit!

Hi. I am Kamille. I am so glad you can come with me on a trip through the phonics zoo! I brought my friend Justin. Let's walk together and see what we can learn.

ZOO

I look to my left and I look to my right. I wonder what Animals are near. Who will be awake in the phonics zoo? Maybe an Alligator will use his large mouth and hissing for us all to hear..

Listen! Do you hear that sound loud and clear? Look! It's a Baboon hitting the wall with his feet. He wants to see us. He jumps from tree to tree, catching limbs to look closer at Justin and me.

“What do you think we will hear next?” I ask Justin.

“I am not sure,” he says. “But I can’t wait to see what we find. Let’s walk some more with our ears open wide.”

The next thing I hear seems very near. “It sounds like a big shuffle or scuffle,” says Justin.

“Wow, what a good call!” says Kamille. Two Chimpanzees are dancing and having a ball!

E

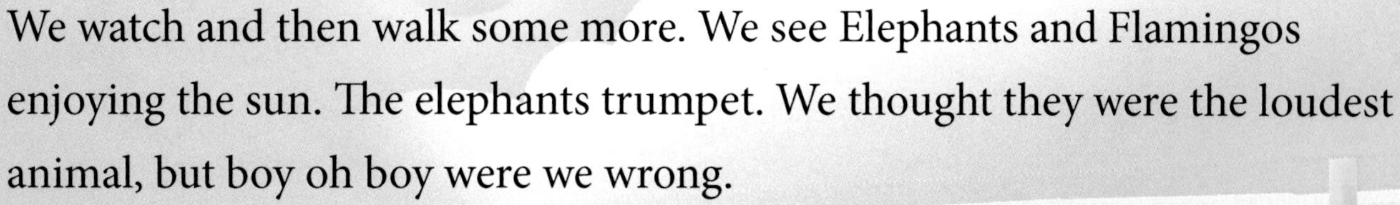

We watch and then walk some more. We see Elephants and Flamingos enjoying the sun. The elephants trumpet. We thought they were the loudest animal, but boy oh boy were we wrong.

The Goats along the way had a lot to say. It sounded like g-g-g0000000. So we kept walking through the phonics zoo.

H

Next we heard something in a lovely field. We saw beautiful Hummingbirds! They hummed in the sun near red roses. Iguanas drank from a pond behind glass, in the water up to their noses.

K
J
L

We kept walking and then saw Jaguars jumping from stone to stone, not trying to stay. Kangaroos were kicking, trying to get away. The jaguars were big, but the lions were bigger and taller. Their roars were loud and strong to match their size. And Ladders on the side for them to use their large feet to climb.

M

The Monkeys were happy to see us. They chattered and showed us things. Like how to dangle and climb and scratch while you swing.
We don't know what comes next, but we are excited to keep walking through the phonics zoo!

It's cool near some large glasses of water. Inside is a big fish with a looooong nose. A Narwhal is looking at us right in the eye! What a way to keep us looking at what is moving by!

The Polar bears are big and white. They sit and look like they could be a fright. But we found out they are just as nice as the otters on the bank beside them.

P

Q

Not just big animals caught our eye. We saw cute little ones like Quails flying through nearby trees. They were quiet as they could be. The Rabbits were quiet too. They jumped and hopped so fast with no hullabaloo.

U
S

But behind the windows we heard Snakes loud and clear. They hissed the sssssss sound when we walked near. We passed them and saw large Tigers. They made us want to stand **T-T-T** tall to be sure we saw it all! One thing is for sure. We should have brought an Umbrella to keep the sun out of our eyes as we walk through the phonics zoo.

At the end of our journey we thought about all the animals that showed us how amazing they are. We discovered sounds and saw some amazing Views. We even saw some Water waves along the way. We went to the eXit to end our day.

exit

Thank You

For Visiting The ZOO

Justin and I think You could find just as many things walking through the phonics Zoo. We are going to visit the world of phonics around our room at school. We sure hope you do too!

Made in the USA
Monee, IL
03 May 2021